READING
SKILLS BOOK

LEVEL 7

Read the story again. Close your book and try to answer the questions without looking. Then check your answers against the book. Answer in sentences.

1   Where was Sam going?

2   What things did Tess like doing?

3   Why did Sam take off his new shoes?

4   What did Sam find for Tess to play with?

5   Why couldn't Sam find his shoes?

6   Why wouldn't Tess come out of the pond?

Oh, Tess!

7 What do you think Sam's parents said to him when he
got home?

8 Draw a picture of how you think Sam looked when he
got home.

1   Write these words in your exercise book in alphabetical order.

(a)   friend   <u>surprise</u>   home   bell   school

(b)   before   <u>catch</u>   books   dog   bad

(c)   along   picture   <u>shout</u>   second   eat

(d)   bark   stop   bump   clean   <u>run</u>

(e)   fast   away   room   dry   <u>trouble</u>

2   List the words that are underlined in alphabetical order.

Find them in a dictionary. Write down what they mean.

3 List these words in alphabetical order.

| bad   picture   stop   fast |

Choose a meaning for each word and write it next to
the right word.

• to end

• not good

• very quick

• a painting

4 These words have two meanings. Write a sentence for
each meaning.

| bark   second |

Read these riddles. Can you guess who they are? Answer in sentences.

1   I live next door to Sam. I am big and brown. I love to swim. Who am I?

2   I live in a flat. I am going away. I want someone to water my plants. Who am I?

3   I am small and furry. I have no family. I would like to live with children. Who am I?

4   I am very large. I have a long neck and a long tail. I frightened a teacher when I went to school. Who am I?

5   I went to school one day. I played with the children. They tried to catch me but I ran away. Who am I?

Now make up riddles for two characters in the book. Try them out on a friend.

Comprehension

All the stories in this book are about pets. Which stories do you think could happen in real life? Answer in sentences.

1 Could the story in "Oh, Tess!" happen in real life? Which parts do you think could or couldn't really happen?

2 In "Cat burglar", what did the burglar think when he heard the noise of the cat walking across the piano? Do you think this is what someone would really think if they heard this noise?

3 Do you think the story of Pickle Monster Mucky Scruff could happen in real life? Do you think a kitten could really understand what people say? Why?

4 "Pets" and "Kim at school" are both about pets visiting school. Do you think either of these could really happen? Why?

The foxes go to town

Read the story again. Close your book and try to answer the questions without looking. Then check your answers against the book.

Answer in sentences.

1   What were the names of the three young foxes?

2   Where was Mr Fox taking his family?

3   Who were the animals with two legs?

4   Why did the foxes have to hide in the grass?

Comprehension

5 Where did the beautiful smell come from that made Bobby feel hungry?

6 Why don't the people like the foxes taking food from their dustbins?

7 Why do you think the foxes went into the town for food?

8 What do you think the foxes find to eat in the dustbins?

The badger

Imagine that you are a young badger. Describe yourself, your home, your family and what you like doing and eating. Use the information in the book to help you.

The questions below might help you too.

- Who are you?
- What do you look like?
- Where do you live? What is it like?
- Who lives with you?
- What do you like to eat?
- What is your favourite food?
- What do you like to do?
- Where and when do you play?

Choose the right word to replace the words that are underlined.
Write the whole sentence in your exercise book.

digging	tunnels	clean	bedding	paw prints

1 Badgers make a sett by <u>using their sharp claws to make holes</u> in the ground.

2 At the end of the <u>long holes in the ground</u> there is a special hole where the badgers sleep.

3 Badgers change the <u>straw that they sleep on</u> when it gets dirty.

4 Badgers like to <u>get rid of the dirt from</u> each other's fur.

5 Sometimes you can see the <u>marks that their feet make</u> in the mud.

Look at the picture on pages 30 and 31.

1   Make a list of all the animals that you can see.

2   Describe what each animal is doing.

3   Make a list of all the pieces of rubbish that you can see.

4   Explain why the rubbish is dangerous.

The school trip

Look at the pictures on pages 2 and 3 of your book.

1 Think of a good title for the pictures. Write it in your exercise book.

2 Describe the clothes the driver is wearing (on page 2).

3 Describe the clothes Miss Hill is wearing (on page 3).

4 Describe what the horse is wearing.

5 How many children can you see in the picture? Write about what they are doing on page 3.

6 Pretend you are one of the children. Write about your trip to the railway park.

Finding words quickly

Sometimes we need to look for special words. We can look quickly just for these words. We don't need to read every word.

1   Look at these words quickly.

A	**B**	**C**	**D**
planet	float	rocks	pipe
earth	fly	air	suit
moon	go	water	food
stars	swim	desert	bag

Now write these words in your exercise book.

| stars | water | bag | air | rocks | planet | swim | food |

Check the lists very quickly to find each word. Write the letter for the list by each word, like this:

stars A

In space

2 List these words in your exercise book.

earth   moon   space   rocket

All of these are in the story. Look quickly along each line of the
story to find the words. How many times is each one used?
Write the number by the words in your list, like this:

earth 4

Mrs Bolter's car

Read the story again. Close your book and try to answer the questions without looking. Then check your answers against the book. Answer in sentences.

1 What sort of car did Mrs Bolter want?

2 What did she see on top of the rubbish tip?

3 What did Mrs Bolter decide to do?

4 What did Mr Khan bring for her?

Mrs Bolter's car

5   How did Mrs Bolter get the rest of the parts that she needed for her car?

6   What did Mrs Bolter need to fix the parts of her car together?

7   Do you think someone could really make a car from old parts on a rubbish tip?

8   Look at the picture on page 21. Do you think this car is like the one that Mrs Bolter described on page 17? Say what is the same and what is different about it.

Answer in sentences.

1   Where did James run away to?

2   How do people travel in Venice?

3   What didn't James like about Venice?

4   What did James see run out of the big church?

5   What happened when James fell?

6   Who pulled James out of the water?

7   What did the gondolier get for James to eat?

8   Why did James decide to stay in Venice?

Comprehension

The haircut

Answer in sentences.

1 Look at the picture on page 2 of your book. Think of a good title for the picture. Write it in your exercise book.

2 Look at the pictures of Mark on page 3 and page 5. Write about how his hair looks on page 3 and how it has changed on page 5.

3 Look at the picture on page 6. There are five people in the picture with Mark. Write about what each person's hair is like.

4 Write about your own hair and say what it looks like. How would you really like it to look?

Read the story again. Close your book and try to answer the
questions without looking. Then check your answers against the book.
Answer in sentences.

1   What is the capital city of Wales?

2   Who built the castles in Wales?

3   Who built Caernarfon Castle?

4   Who can be called the Prince of Wales?

5   What is the highest mountain in Wales called?

6   What is the quickest way to get to the top of Mount Snowdon?

7   What is slate used for?

8   Find a picture of the Welsh flag and draw it in your book.

Comprehension/Information

The Giant's Causeway

What do you know about the characters in this story?

1 Make a list of the characters in the story and write a sentence about each one.

2 Why do you think the Scottish giant started to build a causeway when he heard about Finn MacCool's causeway?

3 What sort of person was Finn MacCool? Explain your answer.

4 What sort of person was the Scottish giant? Explain your answer.

Look at the photographs in the book and read the labels to find out the answers. Answer in sentences

1   How do big boats get through Tower Bridge?

2   Where is the statue of Peter Pan?

3   What is the name of the castle that is on the front cover of the book?

4   What is the name of the castle in Anglesey?

5   Which county is the Giant's Causeway in?

6   What is the Giant's Causeway made from?

7   What sort of animal was Greyfriars Bobby?

8   What is the name of the big show that soldiers put on at Edinburgh Castle?

Read the story again. Close your book and try to answer the questions without looking. Then check your answers against the book.
Answer in sentences.

1 What did Selina see that made her think a hurricane was coming?

2 What three things did Selina and her family do to get ready for the hurricane?

3 What did the family do to pass the time in the cellar?

4 What did Selina think the wind sounded like?

5 What frightened Selina when she was in the cellar?

6 Has Bobby been in a hurricane before? How can you tell?

7 How do you think Grandma felt when she saw her house and garden after the hurricane?

Read the story again. Close your book and try to answer the questions without looking. Then check your answers against the book. Answer in sentences.

1 Where were Kamla and Ajay going on the bus?

2 Who was Satish?

3 How did Satish, Ajay and Kamla get to the market?

4 What did Ajay want to buy?

5 Which season does the Holi festival welcome?

6 How did the children celebrate Holi?

7 What did Mum buy on the last day in India?

Comprehension

Answer in sentences.

1   Look at the pictures of Sophie's dad on pages 22, 28 and 29. Describe what he looks like.

2   Look at the picture on pages 24 and 25. Describe what Mrs Hunter looks like.

3   Look at the picture on page 28. Describe Sophie's clothes.

4   Write about what the men are doing to the sheep.

5   Write down the word in the story that tells you what the people who do this job are called.

6   Look at the picture on page 30. Describe Sophie's bike.

7   Pretend you are Sophie. Write a letter to Mike telling him all about where you live and what you like doing. Don't forget to write your address at the top so that Mike can write back to you.

Answer in sentences.

1 Which person do you think was having the worst day? Why?

2 Would you like to do any of the things that Kenji's family had to do?

3 Which person do you like best in this story? Why?

4 Read the story again and look at the pictures carefully. Which country do you think Kenji lives in? How can you tell?

The story of the the fisherman and his wife could have ended in another way.

1 Think of three different wishes that they could have made. Write them in your exercise book.

2 Do you think these wishes would have made the fisherman and his wife happy or unhappy?

3 Write a different ending to the story using the three wishes that you have thought of. Draw and colour a picture for your story.

4 Write about three wishes that you would make. Say why you would want these wishes to come true.

1 Write these words in alphabetical order.

(a) <u>problem</u> dragon place <u>proud</u> city

(b) chief <u>shame</u> people puppet <u>worried</u>

(c) strong clever <u>wise</u> brave <u>village</u>

(d) house <u>sneak</u> country <u>parade</u> trouble

2 List the words that are underlined in alphabetical order.
Find them in a dictionary. Write down what they mean.

3 List these words in alphabetical order.

city trouble chief clever

Choose a meaning for each word and write it next to the
right word.

- a large town
- a person who is in charge
- something that is a worry
- good at thinking

4 Choose four of the words from the lists in question 1 and write an interesting sentence for each one.

5 Skim through pages 22 and 23. How many times can you find the word "village"?

6 Skim through page 24. How many times can you find the word "chief"?

7 Skim through all the story (pages 22 to 32). How many times can you find the word "dragon"?

Read the story again. Close your book and try to answer the
questions without looking. Then check your answers against the book.
Answer in sentences.

1   What did Tom hear one day as he was walking along?

2   What stange sight did Tom see when he looked through the
        long grass?

3   What did Tom want the leprechaun to do?

4 How did the leprechaun trick Tom?

5 What did the leprechaun tell Tom to do?

6 Why did Tom think that it would be all right to run home for a spade?

7 Why did Tom always listen out for the leprechaun's song?

8 Did the leprechaun keep his promise?

9 Can you think of a way Tom could have made sure he would be able to find the right thistle?

proud sad worried angry happy excited unhappy
frightened silly pleased surprised ashamed

Answer the questions in sentences. The words at the top of the page might help you.

1   How did the fisherman feel when the fish he caught
began to speak?

2   How did the mice feel about putting the bell on the cat?

3   How did the chief feel when he found that no one knew what a
dragon looked like?

4   How did Tom feel when he saw a bright red sock on every
thistle in the field?

5   How do you feel when you have done some very good work?

6   How do you think someone would feel if you caught them doing
something wrong?